The Far Side Observer

The Far Side Observer

BY GARY LARSON

WARNER BOOKS

A *Warner* Book

The Far Side is a cartoon feature created by Gary Larson.
The Far Side Observer was first published in the United States by Andrews McMeel
Publishing, an Andrews McMeel Universal Company, Kansas City, Missouri.

The Far Side Observer © 1987 by FarWorks, Inc.

The Far Side Cartoons © 1985, 1986 and 1987 by FarWorks, Inc.

The Far Side is a registered trademark of FarWorks, Inc. and is registered with the
U.S. Patent and Trademark Office.

First published in Great Britain in 1989 by Futura Publications
Reprinted 1990, 1991 (twice)
This edition published by Warner Books in 1992
Reprinted 1992, 1993, 1994, 1997, 1998.

A CIP catalogue record for this book is available from the British Library.

ISBN 0 7515 0462 9

Printed and bound in Great Britain by
The Guernsey Press Co Ltd, Guernsey, Channel Islands

Warner Books
A Division of
Little, Brown and Company (UK)
Brettenham House
Lancaster Place
London
WC2E 7EN

The Far Side Observer

Washington crossing the street

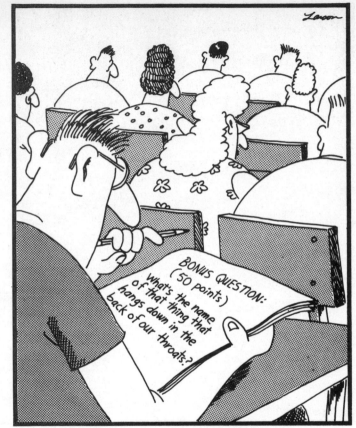

Final page of the Medical Boards

6

"Think about it, Murray. ... If we could get this baby runnin', we could run over hikers, pick up females, chase down mule deer — man, we'd be the grizzlies from hell."

7

The Snakes of War

Okay, you guys — if we're gonna take that hill, we'll have to do it an inch at a time, flat on our bellies, wriggling thru the mud... Think you morons can handle that?

"My God! Willard's home early! Don't move — his vision's not very good, but his sense of smell and hearing are quite acute."

"Hey! That's milk! And you said you were all empty, you stinkin' liar!"

"Holy moley, Loretta! Not only is it still there, look what it did to the end of my stick!"

"Stimulus, response! Stimulus, response! Don't you ever *think*?"

"He's dead, all right — beaked in the back . . . and, you know, this won't be easy to solve."

Inside the sun

In that one split second, when the choir's last note had ended, but before the audience could respond, Vinnie Conswego belches the phrase, "That's all, folks."

"Allen, you jerk! Dad told us not to do that or we'd scare the fish!"

Never put your tongue on a glacier.

"She's lookin' good, Vern!"

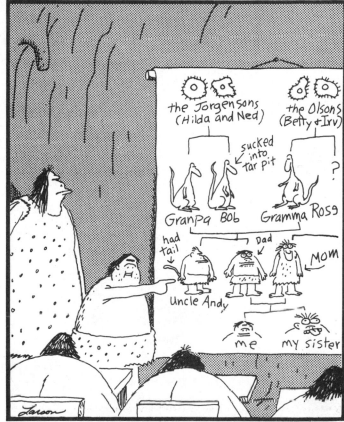

Dirk brings his family tree to class.

"Mr. Osborne, may I be excused? My brain is full."

Well, there goes your brother again... filling the kids' heads with those stories.

...so this package arrives out of no-where--no return address or nothin'... just one word smeared across it--"giblets!"

16

17

Early chemists describe the first dirt molecule.

Volume five in a series

Where "minute" steaks come from

"Of course, long before you mature, most of you will be eaten."

19

Inadvertently, Roy dooms the entire earth to annihilation when, in an attempt to be friendly, he seizes their leader by the head and shakes vigorously.

"Well, wouldn't you know it — we've come all this way to our favorite beach and someone's strung chicken wire around it."

A young Genghis Khan and his Mongol hordette

God as a kid tries to make a chicken in his room.

"Ooo! *This* is always amusing. . . . Here comes Bessie inside her plastic cow ball."

"Go back to sleep, Chuck. You're just havin' a nightmare —
of course, we *are* still in hell."

"Say, ain't you a stranger in this part?"

23

"Ha! Figured you might try escapin', Bert — so I just took the liberty of removin' your horse's brain."

"And now that's the last of that."

24

Suddenly, Dr. Frankenstein realized he had left his brain
in San Francisco.

"Henry! Hurry or you're gonna miss it — ghost riders in the kitchen!"

"Hey! C'mon, Jed! . . . Ease up on them hammers!"

"You wanna have some fun, Fred? Watch . . . Growling and bristling, I'm gonna stand in front of the closet door and just stare."

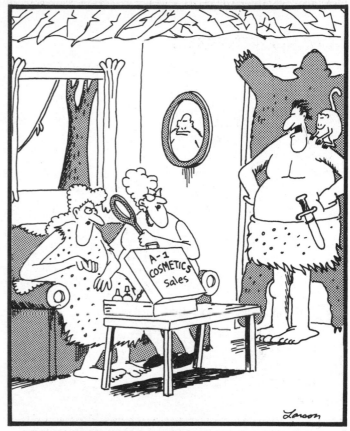

"Whoa! Smells like a French primate house in here."

"Randy! Just sit down, eat your cereal, and look for that thing later!"

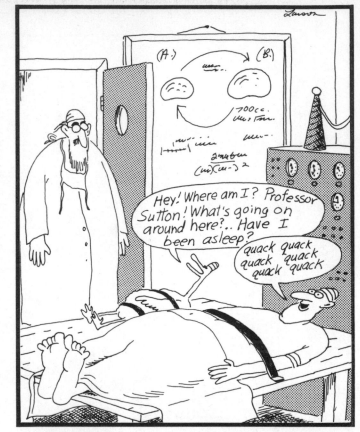

The operation was a success: Later, the duck, with his new human brain, went on to become the leader of a great flock. Irwin, however, was ostracized by his friends and family and eventually just wandered south.

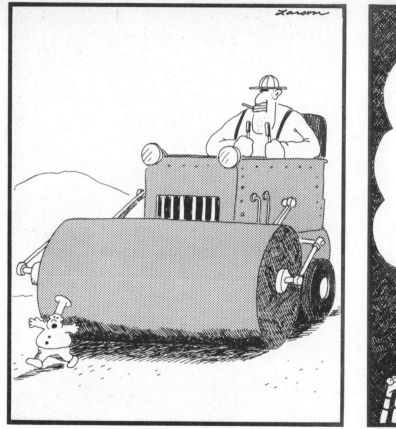

The Pillsbury Doughboy meets Frank's Asphalt and
Concrete Paving Service.

Snake horror stories

"Boy, he even looks like a drowned rat."

The monster snorkel: Allows your child to breathe comfortably without exposing vulnerable parts to an attack.

Classroom afflictions

Early clock-watchers

Dizzy Gillespie's seventh birthday party

Helen paused. With an audible "wumph," Muffy's familiar yipping had ended, and only the sounds of Ed's football game now emanated from the living room.

Midway through the exam, Allen pulls out a bigger brain.

The Hendersons of the jungle

Second to last of the Mohicans

Horror films of the wild

"And here we are last summer going south. . . . Wait a minute, Irene! We went *north* last summer! The stupid slide's in backward!"

"I hear 'em! . . . Gee, there must be a *hundred* of the little guys squirmin' around in there!"

38

"Give me a hand here, Etta . . . I got into a nest of wiener dogs over on Fifth and Maple."

Tantor burns up on I-90.

At the Strategic Pie Limitation Talks

"It's 'Them,' gentlemen."

40

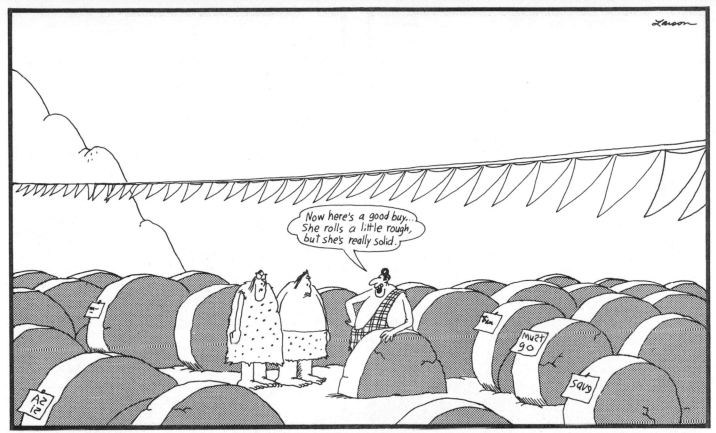

Early wheeler-dealers

Like a lot of dogs, I often have problems finding thrown objects in high grass... That's why I use the new ACME Stick-be-Found.

Dog endorsements

Whale fitness classes

"Barbara! I'm goin' for help — tread soup!"

"Whoa! Watch where that thing lands — we'll probably need it."

Buddy's dreams

"Sorry to bother you, sir, but there's another salesman out here — you want me to tell him to go to heaven?"

Chicken nudist colonies

"So, you're a *real* gorilla, are you? Well, guess you wouldn't mind munchin' down a few beetle grubs, would you? . . . In fact, we wanna see you chug 'em!"

"And another thing! I'm sick and tired of you callin' me 'new kid' all the time!"

"Well, from across the hall I could hear this heated argument, followed by sounds of a scuffle. Suddenly, there was this tremendous, blood-curdling 'quaaaaacck!' That's when I called."

Henry! Look!.. It's a letter from Richard!

PLANKTON IN DECLINE

Moby's parents

47

"How many times did I say it, Harold? How many times? 'Make sure that bomb shelter's got a can opener — ain't much good without a can opener,' I said."

"Look. I'm sorry . . . If you weighed 500 pounds, we'd certainly accommodate you — but it's simply a fact that a *400*-pound gorilla does *not* sleep anywhere he wants to."

49

"Just think . . . Here we are, the afternoon sun beating down on us, a dead, bloated rhino underfoot, and good friends flying in from all over. . . . I tell you, Ed, this is the best of times."

The Headless Horsefamily

"Well, Roger's hoping for a male and I'd like a little female. . . . But, really, we'll both be content if it just has six eyes and eight legs."

To win the tribe's respect, Jed first had to defeat their best thumb-wrestler.

The portrait of Dorian Cow

Some of the non-vital organs

"It's Bob, all right . . . but look at those vacuous eyes, that stupid grin on his face — he's been domesticated, I tell you."

54

"You sure you're supposed to be doin' that, Mitch?"

55

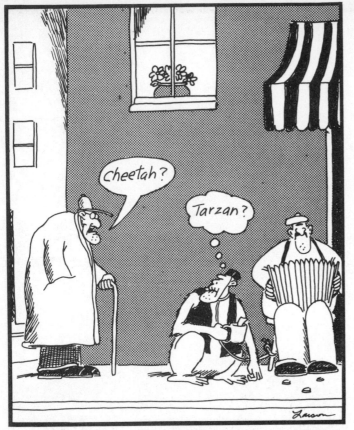

Their reunion was both brief and awkward — each still bearing the wounds from that ugly "Jane incident."

Professor Gallagher and his controversial technique of simultaneously confronting the fear of heights, snakes, and the dark.

Buffalo dares

Life on a microscope slide

"Maybe it's *not* me, y'know? . . . Maybe it's the *rest* of the herd that's gone insane."

Snake inventors

The embarrassment of riding off into a fake sunset

Thomas Sullivan, a blacksmith who attended the original Thanksgiving dinner, is generally credited as being the first person to stick olives on all his fingers.

"I'm sorry, ma'am, but his license does check out and, after all, your husband *was* in season. Remember, just because he knocks doesn't mean you have to let him in."

62

"Yeah. My boss don't appreciate me either. To him I'm just a gofer. 'Igor! Go for dead bodies! . . . Igor! Go for brains! . . . Igor! Go for dead bodies!' I dunno — give me another beer."

"Uh-oh, Danny. Sounds like the monster in the basement has heard you crying again. . . . Let's be reaaaal quiet and hope he goes away."

Snake weight-rooms

"For heaven's sake, Henry, tell the kids a *pleasant* story for once — they don't always have to hear the one about your head."

Onward they pushed, through the thick, steamy jungle, separately ruing the witch doctor's parting words: "Before you leave this valley, each of you will be wearing a duck."

"Chief say, 'Someone . . . here . . . walk . . . through . . . buffalo . . . field.'"

"Listen — just take one of our brochures and see what we're all about. . . . In the meantime, you may wish to ask yourself, 'Am I a happy cow?'"

Non-singing canaries have to take wood shop.

"He's got one shot left, Murray — and then he's *ours!*"

"Somethin's up, Jake. . . . That's Ben Potter's horse, all right, but ain't that Henry Morgan's chicken ridin' him?"

"It's this new boyfriend, dear. . . . I'm just afraid one day your father's going to up and blow him away."

Simultaneously all three went for the ball, and the coconut-like sound of their heads colliding secretly delighted the bird.

Unbeknownst to most historians, Einstein started down the road of professional basketball before an ankle injury diverted him into science.

Suddenly, everyone turned and looked — there, standing in the doorway, was one wretched, mean-looking ingrown.

"You know, Russell, you're a great torturer. I mean, you can make a man scream for mercy in nothing flat . . . but boy, you sure can't make a good cup of coffee."

"You idiot! Don't write that down — his name ain't
Puddin' Tame!"

"Forget these guys."

Poodles of the Serengeti

The ghost of Baron Rudolph von Guggenheim, 16th-century nobleman murdered by the Countess Rowena DuBois and her lover (believed to be the Duke of Norwood), falls into Edna's bean dip.

74

Amoeba conventions

" 'You have a small capacity for reason, some basic tool-making skills, and the use of a few simple words.' . . . Yep. That's you."

"Raised the ol' girl from a cub, I did. . . . 'Course, we had to get a few things straight between us. She don't try to follow me into town anymore, and I don't try and take her food bowl away 'til she's done."

"See Dick run. See Jane run. Run run run. See the wolves chase Dick and Jane. Chase chase chase. . . ."

"Oh! *Four* steps to the left and *then* three to the right! . . . What kind of a dance was *I* doing?"

Deer grandmothers

"Primordial soup again?"

"Ooo! Now here's a nice one we built last fall."

"Well, that about does it for the nose — I'm starting to hit cartilage."

When a body meets a body comin' through the rye . . .

"Horse! . . . Is there a man called 'Horse' in here?"

Cartoon teen-agers

"Look. Why don't you just give yourself up quietly? . . .
Otherwise, this thing could turn into a frenzy — and
nobody wants that."

"Well, guess who's home a little early from today's castle siege?"

"I tell you, a crib is just plain worthless — what we need around here is a good cardboard box."

Tarzan is greeted by the Parakeet People.

"Well, shoot! There's my herd! . . . Thank you anyway, ma'am."

The Greystokes at marriage counseling

"Louis . . . phonecaw."

"So, Raymond . . . Linda tells us you work in the security division of an automobile wreckage site."

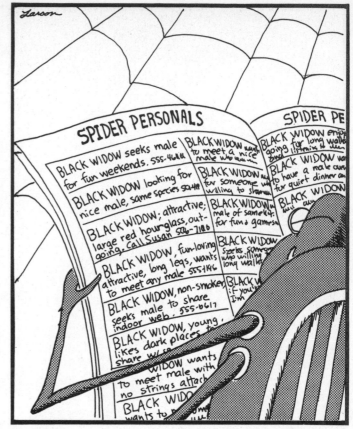

In the early days, living in their squalid apartment, all three shared dreams of success. In the end, however, Bob the Spoon and Ernie the Fork wound up in an old silverware drawer, and only Mac went on to fame and fortune.

Chicken cults

"Just a word of warning, Myron — if you miss, I'm comin' after your big hazel."

And for two excruciating months, he was simply known as "Skinhead of the Jungle."

Seconds later, Mrs. Norton was covered with ink.

"Skunk sandwich, Bill . . . mmmmm . . . skunk sandwich.
. . . Trade for that banana?"

"Mom said no sitting on the edge, Wayne."

Custer's last view

Wendall Zurkowitz: Slave to the waffle light

Bobbing for poodles

When potato salad goes bad

"There it is again . . . a feeling that in a past life I was someone named Shirley MacLaine."

"Oh, Ginger — you look absolutely stunning . . . and whatever you rolled in sure does stink."

Night of the Living Dead Chipmunks

"Yo! Farmer Dave! Let's go, let's go, let's go! . . . You gettin' up with us chickens or not?"

PULL

MIDVALE
SCHOOL FOR
THE GIFTED

"Airrrrr spearrrr . . . airrrrr spearrrr! . . ."

"My boy made the frame."

Business lunch

The door swung wide, and there, to the horror of the other pirates, stood Captain Monet — unmistakable with his one eye and pegbody.

Only they know the difference.

Bobo remained free the rest of his life, although he did
find it necessary to seek counseling.

Breakfast on other planets

"So, until next week — Adios, amoebas."

☐ THE CHICKENS ARE RESTLESS	GARY LARSON	£5.99
☐ WIENER DOG ART	GARY LARSON	£6.99
☐ UNNATURAL SELECTIONS	GARY LARSON	£6.99
☐ COWS OF OUR PLANET	GARY LARSON	£6.99
☐ THE CURSE OF MADAM "C"	GARY LARSON	£5.99
☐ THE FAR SIDE	GARY LARSON	£4.99
☐ IN SEARCH OF THE FAR SIDE	GARY LARSON	£4.99
☐ BRIDE OF THE FAR SIDE	GARY LARSON	£4.99
☐ VALLEY OF THE FAR SIDE	GARY LARSON	£4.99
☐ HOUND OF THE FAR SIDE	GARY LARSON	£4.99
☐ IT CAME FROM THE FAR SIDE	GARY LARSON	£4.99
☐ BEYOND THE FAR SIDE	GARY LARSON	£4.99
☐ NIGHT OF THE CRASH-TEST DUMMIES	GARY LARSON	£4.99
☐ WILDLIFE PRESERVES	GARY LARSON	£4.99
☐ THE FAR SIDE GALLERY	GARY LARSON	£8.99
☐ THE FAR SIDE GALLERY 2	GARY LARSON	£8.99
☐ THE FAR SIDE GALLERY 3	GARY LARSON	£8.99
☐ THE FAR SIDE GALLERY 4	GARY LARSON	£8.99
☐ THE FAR SIDE GALLERY 5	GARY LARSON	£8.99
☐ THE PRE-HISTORY OF THE FAR SIDE	GARY LARSON	£9.99
☐ LAST CHAPTER AND WORSE	GARY LARSON	£6.99
☐ THERE'S A HAIR IN MY DIRT	GARY LARSON	£9.99

Warner Books now offer an exciting range of quality titles by both established and new authors which can be ordered from the following address:
Little, Brown and Company (UK),
P.O. Box 11,
Falmouth
Cornwall
E:Mail: books@barni.avel.co.uk
Fax No: 01326 317444
Telephone No: 01326 372400

Payments can be made as follows: cheque, postal order (payable to Little, Brown and Company) or by credit cards, Visa/Access. Do not send cash or currency. UK customers and B.F.P.O. please allow £1.00 for postage and packing for the first book, plus 50p for the second book, plus 30p for each additional book up to a maximum charge of £3.00 (7 books plus).

Overseas customers including Ireland, please allow £2.00 for the first book, plus £1.00 for the second book, plus 50p for each additional book.

NAME (Block Letters) ....

....

ADDRESS ....

....

....

☐ I enclose my remittance for _____

☐ I wish to pay by Access/Visa Card

Number | | | | | | | | | | | | | | | |

Card Expiry Date | | | | |